The World Around Me

The publisher gratefully acknowledges the kind permission granted to reprint the following copyrighted material. Should any copyright holder have been inadvertently omitted, they should apply to the publisher, who will be pleased to credit them in full in any subsequent editions.

8 7 6 5 4 3 2 1

ISBN: 0-7853-3903-5

The World Around Me

Adapted by Lynne Suesse

Cover illustrated by Judith Pfeiffer, Linda Prater

Interior illustrated by
Judith Pfeiffer, Tish Tenud,
Christina Ong, Anne O'Connor

Publications International, Ltd.

Jesus Loves the Little Children

Jesus loves the little children,
All the children of the world.
Red and yellow, black and white,
They are precious in His sight.
Jesus loves the little children
of the world.

5

6

The Lord is good to me,
and so I thank the Lord
for giving me the things
I need: the sun, the rain,
and the apple seed!
The Lord is good to me.

Dear God,
I'm glad the sky is painted blue,
  And the earth is painted green,
With such a lot of nice fresh air
  All sandwiched in-between.

Thank God for rain and
the beautiful rainbow colors.
And thank God for letting
children splash in puddles.

I never spoke with God,
  Nor visited in heaven;
Yet certain am I of the spot
  As if the chart were given.

Emily Dickinson

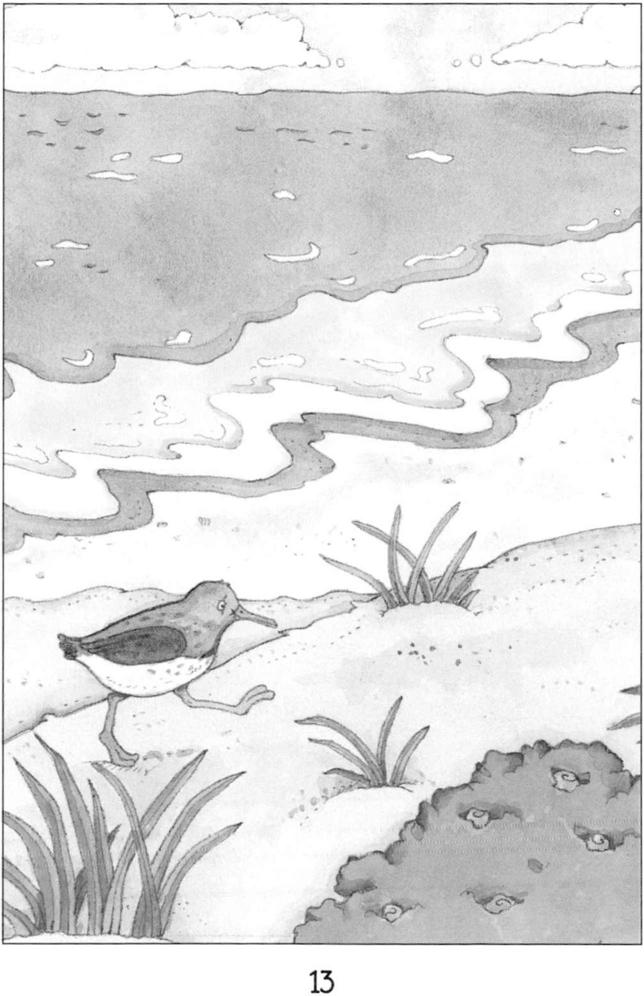

God made the sun,
    And God made the trees.
God made the mountains,
    And God made me.

All things bright and beautiful,
　All creatures great and small,
All things wise and wonderful,
　The Lord God made them all.

Cecil Frances Alexander

Music is the art of the prophets, the only art that can calm the agitations of the soul: it is one of the most magnificent and delightful presents God has given us.

Martin Luther

Dear Father, hear and bless
    The beasts and singing birds.
And guard with tenderness
    Small things that have no words.

He prayeth best, who loveth best
  All things both great and small;
For the dear God who loveth us,
  He made and loveth all.

The love of God is shown
in the beauty of the earth.

Amen.